The New Girl

by Daniel Dee
illustrated by Carolina Arentsen

**Harcourt**

Orlando   Boston   Dallas   Chicago   San Diego

Visit *The Learning Site!*

www.harcourtschool.com

Even though she had been there a week, Caroline was still uncomfortable in her new school. To her dismay, she had no friends to talk to or hang out with.

Back in Alabama, it had been different, because there she had lots of friends. Here in California, the kids didn't seem to be as friendly. Nobody came up to her as she sat alone during recess—again. Caroline had never felt so lonely in her life.

It was hard to meet people because she was a bit shy. She didn't feel comfortable starting conversations with people she didn't know. In Alabama, she had known the same group of kids all her life, so her shyness hadn't been a problem.

It was also hard to adapt to the system at her new school. She didn't spend the whole day in the same classroom with the same kids. For certain classes, such as Spanish, art, and music, she had to go to different rooms and get used to different teachers.

It would have been fun, she supposed, if she had friends in each class, but it just made Caroline feel even lonelier to go to her different classes all day by herself.

One evening, when her mom was getting ready to start dinner, she asked Caroline how school was going. "Have you started to make any new friends, dear?" she asked.

"Nobody likes me," moaned Caroline. "I'm totally despised at school. I hate it here! Why did we ever move?"

"Come on, Caroline. It can't be that bad. I'm sure it's just that the other students don't know you yet. Have you tried to talk to anybody?"

"No, not yet. But no one's tried to talk to me, either."

"Well, maybe you should make the first move. You might be astonished to find out how friendly people can be if you start talking to them first," Mrs. Nott said.

"I suppose you're right, Mom. But it's easier said than done. What am I going to say?"

"Just be yourself and you'll do fine. Talk to someone about the homework assignments or about one of your classes. It will take time, but you'll find someone to be friends with."

"OK, Mom. Thanks for the advice."

The next day on the way to her homeroom, Caroline spotted a sign-up sheet for the girls' soccer team. She wrote down the tryout time in her notebook. Maybe joining the soccer team would be a good way to meet someone. Besides, soccer was fun.

Caroline's first class was history. Suzie sat at the desk in front of her. At the end of class, Suzie handed her the homework assignment that the teacher was passing to each row.

"Hey, thanks," Caroline muttered.

In the hallway later, Caroline saw Suzie walking to her next class and thought she'd try to get to know her better. She caught up with her. "Hey, Suzie, can you believe that assignment Mr. Iverson handed us? An entire chapter is a ton of work! I guess I know what we're doing this weekend."

"How do you know my name?" asked Suzie.

"You sit right in front of me in class."

"Oh yeah! What's your name?"

"My name is Caroline. I'm new here."

"You sure have a funny way of talking. Where are you from?" asked Suzie.

"I'm from Alabama. It sure is different here in California. I think you're the first person I've talked to, except for teachers. Everyone else has been totally ignoring me. Do I look weird or something?" Caroline asked jokingly.

"No, of course not. Caroline, can I be honest with you? Some of the kids have been wondering whether you're a snob. They think you act as if you're too good to talk to anybody."

"What? I can hardly believe that! I'm not a snob. I'm just kind of quiet, that's all. It's hard because I don't know anybody here," said Caroline, showing her dismay. "I'm completely astonished, Suzie. Thanks for telling me. I will make more of an effort to talk to people from now on."

"No problem. Well, here's my next class. See you later," said Suzie.

At the soccer tryouts later that afternoon, Caroline made a point to talk to the other girls as they waited for the coach. After the tryouts, Caroline felt confident that she had made the cut. However, she knew she'd have to wait for the coach to announce who was on the team. Then she would buy a soccer ball for practicing at home.

After dinner that night, Caroline opened her history book. The chapter was about President Franklin Delano Roosevelt. She started to read about what an interesting President he had been.

As she read, Caroline was shocked to find out that Roosevelt had been stricken with polio eleven years before he became President of the United States. It was interesting to read about the agreement he had with the press. To hide his immobility, the press photographed him only from the waist up. Photographs showing his leg braces or his wheelchair were very rare.

After she read the chapter, Caroline took a break to talk to her parents.

"Mom, I was wrong about the kids at school. It isn't that they despise me. They think I'm a snob, though. Can you believe that?"

"How did you find that out?" asked her mom.

"Suzie, from my history class, told me today. I'm working on changing their opinion of me."

"That's the spirit, Caroline!" her dad said.

The next day in her Spanish class, the teacher called on Caroline. She asked her to decipher the first two paragraphs for everyone. Caroline translated everything as if she'd been studying Spanish for years.

"Grácias, Señorita Nott. Muy bien," said Señora Crupi.

"No problema, maestra," said Caroline as she sat down in her seat. Some of the other kids laughed.

After Spanish class, a boy came up to
her to tell her what a great job she had
done. "*Hola*," he said in Spanish. Then,
switching to English, he asked, "What's
your name?"

"Caroline. What's yours?"

"Jason. Say, Caroline, do you think
you could help me with Spanish? I don't
know what I would do if Señora Crupi
asked me to decipher anything in the
book. It's too difficult. I just don't under-
stand it."

"I'll be glad to help you, Jason. What are you doing this weekend? Our first quiz is Monday, you know."

"Yeah, that's what I'm afraid of," said Jason.

As they exchanged phone numbers, Suzie came up to her.

"Come on, Alabama girl, we'll be late for history class!" said Suzie in a friendly voice.

"I guess we'd better get going," said Caroline. Then, turning to Jason, she said, "I have to go, Jason. Give me a call tonight, OK?"

"Sure. See you."

"So, Suzie," said Caroline as they hurried to class, "did you read the chapter last night?"

"Yes. Wasn't that sad about Roosevelt's polio? The press was cool not to show his immobility to the public. I wonder how people would have reacted if they had been aware of it."

"Good question! I don't know. Hey, what are you doing after school? Do you want to come over to my house?"

"Sure, Caroline. I'll have to call my mom first. Let's meet by the front door at three o'clock."

Caroline smiled. It looked as though she'd adjust to life in California after all.